TIME to be AWESOME

Stick
your photo
here!

This book belongs to: .....h u c y.....m c D o n a g h.....

PaRRagon

Bath • New York • Cologne • Melbourne • Delhi
Hong Kong • Shenzhen • Singapore

HI THERE!

I'm Twilight Sparkle, and this is YOUR friendship journal!
As the official Princess of Friendship I know just how
important it is to share good times and giggles with
the ponies you love, so inside you'll find plenty
of games, quizzes and space for your
special photos. Oh, AND super-fun party
ideas (happy now, Pinkie Pie?!).
The Mane 6 want to know all about you,
so what are you waiting for?

Love from,

Twilight Sparkle

Friendship

All about ME

Stick a photo of yourself here!

Name:
Lucy

Nickname:
Lucy Loo

Age:
5

Hair colour:
red

Eye colour:
blue

What's your favourite food?:
Chip

What's your favourite colour?:
puple

Who's your favourite pony?:
thilight

List 3 things that are AWESOME about you: Sprakle

I have the best big siter.

my hair is long.

I have playhouse in my garden.

Do you prefer:
- ✓ Parties
- ☐ Snuggly nights in

Which is more fun:
- ✓ Playing sport
- ☐ Reading

What's your favourite:
- ☐ Savoury snacks
- ✓ Sweet treats

Would you rather:
- ☐ Be invisible
- ✓ Be able to fly

MY MANE 5

We want to get to know y'all!

Everypony needs best friends! List your Mane 5 here:

1. ....
2. ....
3. ....
4. ....
5. ....

One of the greatest things about friendship is sharing — whether it's cupcakes, adventures or secrets. Share this book with your friends by asking them to each fill in a profile.

Name: Lucy

Nickname: Lacy Loo

Age: 5

Favourite colour: puple

Favourite pony: tinilight sprakle

Stick a photo of yourself here!

List 3 things that are AWESOME about you:

....

....

....

Would you rather have:
- ○ A magic horn
- ✓ Wonderful wings

Name: ....

Nickname: ....

Age: ....

Favourite colour: ....

Favourite pony:...

List 3 things that are AWESOME about you:

....

....

....

Stick a photo of yourself here!

Would you prefer to be:
○ A Seapony
○ A Pegasus

Name: ....

Nickname: ....

Age: ....

Favourite colour: ....

Favourite pony:...

List 3 things that are AWESOME about you:

....

....

....

Stick a photo of yourself here!

Would you rather live:
○ In a castle
○ On a farm

Name: ....

Nickname: ....

Age: ....

Favourite colour: ....

Favourite pony:......................................

List 3 things that are AWESOME about you:

....

....

....

Stick a photo of yourself here!

Which is cuter:
- ⭕ A rainbow mane
- ⭕ A glittery tail

Name: ....

Nickname: ....

Age: ....

Favourite colour: ....

Favourite pony: ....

List 3 things that are AWESOME about you:

....

....

....

Stick a photo of yourself here!

Your party would have:
- ⭕ A cake cannon
- ⭕ A sonic rainboom

Our friendship story

All friendships have a great story to go with them. What's yours?

How did you all meet?

....

....

....

....

Place? Time? Year? TELL US EVERYTHING!

....

Choose a name for your friendship group:

....

What did you think of everyone at first?

....

....

....

....

Draw a special symbol for your friendship group!

Tick the things you like to do together:

- ⭕ Go shopping
- ⭕ Laugh
- ⭕ Bake
- ⭕ Sports
- ⭕ Play outside
- ⭕ Give each other makeovers
- ⭕ Chat
- ⭕ Sing
- ⭕ Watch TV or films
- ⭕ Have parties
- ⭕ Dance
- ⭕ Share secrets
- ⭕ Listen to music

LOOKING FABULOUS!

Make your very own friendship gallery by sticking your favourite pictures of you and your friends here.

which pony ARE YOU?

Everypony is special, and has lots of qualities that make them unique — just like you! Take this quiz to find out which pony pal you're most like.

Which of these words would you use to describe yourself?

a Clever   b Fun   c Brave   d Shy   e Hard-working   f Creative

How would your friends describe you?

a Organized and patient   b Outgoing and spontaneous   c Confident and daring

d Gentle and kind   e Down-to-earth and dependable   f Generous and inventive

What is your favourite thing to do with your friends?

a Discuss books or do homework   b Gossip in your bedroom or listen to music

c Do something active like playing sport   d Play with pets or volunteer at an animal sanctuary

e Bake something yummy or go for a walk   f Try on different outfits and take photos

Which of these colours do you like best?

a Purple   b Pink   c Blue   d Yellow   e Orange   f Silver

What would you like to be when you're older?

a A teacher   b A party planner   c An athlete

d A vet   e A farmer   f A fashion designer

What is your best skill?

a Reading and learning new things   b Telling jokes and making people laugh

c Games and sports   d Taking care of animals   e Cooking or baking

f Fashion, hair and make-up

ANSWERS:

Mostly As

You are super-smart, and love to read and learn. You are a natural leader and will do anything for your friends — just like Twilight Sparkle!

Mostly Bs

Like Pinkie Pie, you have lots of energy and you're always smiling. You love parties, and are often found entertaining your friends or making them laugh.

Mostly Cs

You are brave, athletic and always up for an adventure. You can seem tough, but like Rainbow Dash are a softie with your friends.

Mostly Ds

You're kind and gentle, and you like to take care of others — especially animals. Though you are sometimes shy, you always stand up for your friends when they need you, just like Fluttershy.

Mostly Es

Like Applejack, you're hard-working, reliable, and a loyal friend. You love the outdoors and can often be found enjoying nature and taking care of the environment.

Mostly Fs

You are fashionable and creative, just like Rarity. You always know the latest fashions and hairstyles, and love to give your friends advice and makeovers.

Now that you know which pony you're most like, which would you pick as your BFF?

....

Get your friends to take the quiz, and record which ponies they are here:

....

....

The *friendship* Pledge

Having a close group of friends is heaps of fun, but everypony disagrees sometimes! Discuss with your pals which of these things you think is most important in a friend.

- ⭘ Listening to others
- ⭘ Sharing your lunch
- ⭘ Keeping friends' secrets
- ⭘ Paying others compliments
- ⭘ Being kind
- ⭘ Compromising
- ⭘ Doing what your friends want to do

- ⭘ Sticking up for yourself
- ⭘ Keeping promises
- ⭘ Being honest
- ⭘ Not leaving anypony out
- ⭘ Putting yourself first
- ⭘ Having fun
- ⭘ Giving good advice

What else makes a great friend?

....

....

....

....

....

Have you ever argued with a friend?

⭘ Yes   ⭘ No

How would you solve an argument?

....

....

Twilight Sparkle is looking for new apprentices to become Princesses of Friendship, and she's chosen YOU! Now that you've agreed on what makes a good friend, all you have to do is fill in this pledge, adding your new group name to the top.

We, ... , solemnly promise to be the best friends we can be.

We will always .... ,

and will never ....

We promise to share .... and .... ,

even if .... !

Our friendship is so special to us because .... ,

and being together makes us feel ....

Most of all, we pony-promise that we will be best friends forever!

Ask your friends to sign the pledge, too!

Signed by,

....

....

....

....

....

....

Congratulations! You're now all officially my princesses-in-training!

Friendship Festival

Friendships like yours should be celebrated! Organize a special Friendship Festival party, choosing a job for each of your friends to help with. Most importantly, have fun!

Start by deciding when and where your party will be.

Did somepony say **PARTY**?!

It will be at:...

On: ....

Then send invitations, using coloured pencils to decorate them. Write your guest list here:

....

....

....

....

.... will be in charge of music.

How about creating a totally awesome playlist for the party?

It would be kind to pick songs everypony likes. **yay!**

....

....

....

....

......................will be in charge of food and drink.   Toffee apples would sure be nice!
What treats will you eat?

....

....

How about pin the tail on the pony? Or turn the page for an EVEN GREATER game!

....
will be in charge of entertainment.
List some ideas here for games and activities:

....

....

....

.... will be in charge of the theme.   Fancy dress would be simply fabulous!
What will the dress code be?

....

....

Rainbow balloons all the way!

....

.... will be in charge of decorations.
How will you make your party look *awesome*?

....

....

....

Pinkie Pie's
WOULD YOU RATHER?

Play Pinkie Pie's super-fun game at your Friendship Festival for guaranteed giggles!
Take it in turns to ask a question below, starting each with "Would you rather ..."

Have to speak in rhyme or be silent for a WHOLE day?

Have hair made of candyfloss or lollipops for fingers?

Live where the clouds rained chocolate milk or lemonade?

Be stuck in a room with Grubber or the Storm King?

Own so many puppies that you could never POSSIBLY stroke them all, or have no puppies at all?

Be completely bald or have hair so long you trip over it?

Wear shoes a size too big or a size too small?

Get shot out of a cake cannon or dive off a waterfall?

Spend a day with the pirates or the Seaponies?

Control the sun like Princess Celestia or the moon like Princess Luna?

AM EFFORT

Working together can be lots of fun. Colour in one half of the pony below then cover it with a piece of paper. Ask a friend to colour in the other half, then remove the paper to reveal your joint creation!

Every princess needs a crown! To add the finishing touch to your party, create tiaras for each of your guests to wear. Cut out this template and trace the shape on to thin card as many times as you need. Decorate with coloured pencils or your stickers, then fasten ribbon to the ends and tie to fit each princess.

AWESOME

ony. Where does she live? What does she like?

I live in fairy world.
I like pizza, chip and flower.

Memory lane

The Mane 6 have had lots of adventures together, and they love to laugh about some of their close calls! Ask your friends and family about their favourite memory of you, and write down what they say:

This is .... 's favourite memory of me:

....

....

....

This is .... 's favourite memory of me:

....

....

....

This is .... 's favourite memory of me:

....

....

....

This is .... 's favourite memory of me:

....

....

....

This is .... 's favourite memory of me:

....

....

....

This is .... 's favourite memory of me:

....

....

....

Rainbow Dash is thinking about some of her favourite friendship memories:

Escaping from Tempest TWICE. We rule!

Helping the pirates get their mojo back.

Becoming Seaponies and racing underwater.

What's the funniest thing that's ever happened to you and your friends?

....

....

Hiding in a giant cake together!

What's the nicest thing a friend has ever done for you?

....

....

Which memory makes you all warm and fuzzy inside?

....

....

....

....

Do you have any embarrassing friendship memories?

....

....

....

....

Have you and your friends ever got into trouble? Do tell!

....

....

WHO SAID THAT?

Each of the Mane 6 represents a different Element of Harmony, and they have their own unique personalities. But how well do you know them? Try to match these quotes with the correct pony.

1 You know what they say — where there's a city, there's a SPA!

2 Pinkie, quit lookin' so happy! Y'ain't foolin' nopony!

3 I'm excited! Who's excited?! AHH, I've never been so excited!!!!

4 You can either let some hoity-toity Storm King tell you how to live your lives or ... you can be awesome again!

5 You seem tense. Do you wanna talk about it?

6 More friends are definitely merrier.

ANSWERS: 1. Rarity 2. Applejack 3. Pinkie Pie 4. Rainbow Dash 5. Fluttershy 6. Twilight Sparkle

Do you and your pals have any favourite sayings? Write them down here:

....

....

....

What are the funniest things that you and your friends have said?

Use this space to remember the nicest things your friends have said to you:

....

....

....

....

....

Yay!

A SECOND CHANCE

It turns out that all Tempest needed was kindness to change her ways. The power of friendship should never be underestimated!

Write about a time you had an argument with a friend:

....

....

How would you resolve an argument?
○ Back down   ○ Try to compromise

....

....

How did you fix it, or are you still not friends?

....

....

....

....

If you're friends again, is there anything you could have done differently?
If you haven't, what could you do to make up?

....

....

....

What is most important after a fight?
○ Admitting you were wrong
○ Saying sorry

....

Fluttershy's friendship tips

Some ponies find it harder to make friends than others. Fluttershy is a quiet pony, but she knows that the smallest acts of kindness can make others feel welcome. Use her tips to make new friends — the more the merrier!

It would be super-nice to try these out on somepony who looks lonely. Tick the ones you use!

○ Smile. Sometimes that's all it takes!

○ Don't join in if others are being mean to somepony. Stick up for them, or find something kind to say.

○ Go and sit or stand next to somepony who is alone.

○ Start a conversation. If you're not sure what to talk about, you could ask them about their hobbies or the music they like.

○ Offer to help with something. This could be anything from lending a pen to helping with homework!

○ Make them smile. You could crack a joke or tell them something funny that's happened to you.

○ Tell them about yourself. Getting to know each other is a great step towards friendship!

○ Ask them questions, but only if they seem comfortable answering.

○ Invite them to join in with your other friends.

Find your friendship score

Twilight Sparkle has found a calculation that lets you see your secret friendship score!

1 First, write "THE MAGIC OF FRIENDSHIP" on a piece of paper.

2 Then write your name underneath, and count how many times each letter of your name appears in "THE MAGIC OF FRIENDSHIP". Make sure you record the number under each letter.

3 Add up the numbers underneath your name. If you get a double figure, add those two numbers together so you're left with a single number (for example, 15 would become 6).

4 Now choose a friend, and repeat these steps with their name.

5 To find your secret friendship score, put the two numbers next to each other — so if your number is 6 and your friend's is 5, you have a friendship score of 65%!

Here's an example to help you:

THE MAGIC OF FRIENDSHIP

R A R I T Y = 7
111310

F L U T T E R S H Y = 9
1001121120

Secret friendship score: 79%

Friendship score 0-25%

You and your pal still have lots to learn about each other, and can become even greater friends by spending quality time together. What a great excuse for a day out!

Friendship score 26-50%

You're pretty firm friends already, but you might not always agree on everything. It's great to be different, just make sure you always listen to each other and you'll be best buddies in no time.

Friendship score 51-75%

You guys are great friends and always keep each other's secrets. You can go that extra mile by being kind to each other even when you're feeling grumpy!

Friendship score 76-100%

You're practically sisters, and know you can always rely on the other for advice, support and lots of giggles. A friendship like yours is truly special!

Use this space to record your results!

Wonderful windows

Princess Celestia keeps a record of important people and events in the stained glass windows of Canterlot Castle. Create your own windows by drawing the special people in your life — and the faraway places you'd love to visit one day.

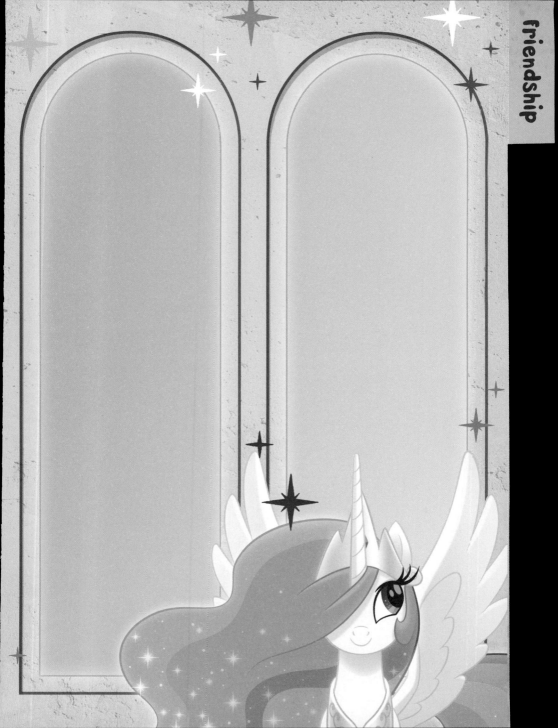

Birthday calendar

Part of being a good friend is remembering your pals' birthdays — giving somepony a homemade card can make them feel really special. Write down your best friends' birthdays below so you'll never forget them.

Name: ....
Birthday: ....
Gift ideas: ....
....
....

Name: ....
Birthday: ....
Gift ideas: ....
....
....

Name: ....
Birthday: ....
Gift ideas: ....
....
....

Name: ....
Birthday: ....
Gift ideas: ....
....
....

Name: ....
Birthday: ....
Gift ideas: ....
....
....

Baking a cake for your best friend would be AWESOME!

Pony tail *friendship* bracelets

Surprise your pals with these special friendship bracelets, or make them together at your next sleepover!

Step 1 Choose ribbon in three colours that you think represent your friend. Does she love nature like Fluttershy, or is she girly like Pinkie?

Step 2 Cut the three ribbons into equal lengths. You'll need at least enough to go round your wrist three times, but cut extra if you're not sure.

Step 3 Hold your three pieces of ribbon in one hand, and tie a knot in the end to fasten them together. Tape down this end, then spread each piece out so you can see them all clearly.

Step 4

Start with piece A on the left, and take it over the piece in the middle, piece B. Lay it down there, so that A now becomes the middle piece.

B   A C

Step 5

Now lift piece C on the right, and take that over piece A. Piece C is now in the middle.

B C A

Step 6

Repeat steps 4 and 5 by alternating between taking the left piece to the middle and then the right, until you have a simple plait.

Step 7 Keep plaiting until the bracelet is long enough to fit round your wrist, and then tie a knot in the end. Leave a long trail of ribbon at the end of the knot — this is the tail, and will help your friend tie their bracelet, as well as looking cute!

FRIENDS FOREVER

With a bit of effort, friendships really can last forever! You and your friends will each have your own adventures, but the memories you share together will always be carried in your hearts. Make sure you never forget them by creating a plan to meet ten years from now.

The date now is: ....

Our ten-year reunion will be on: ....

What time?: .... Where we'll meet: ....

What we'll do: ....

....

Some special moments to remember:

....

....

....

Woo-hoo!
Go friendship!

We PONY-PROMISE to attend our friendship reunion!

Signed: ....

....

....

Faraway adventures

The ponies love visiting new places and going on exciting adventures, even when they haven't planned to! Stick some photos here from your favourite trips to help you treasure the memories forever.

Place: .... Date: ....
Who is in the photo: ....
Why it was awesome: ....

Place: .... Date: ....
Who is in the photo: ....
Why it was awesome: ....

Place: .... Date: ....
Who is in the photo: ....
Why it was awesome: ....

Place: .... Date: ....
Who is in the photo: ....
Why it was awesome: ....

An adventure can be made even more magical by making a new friend, just like Pinkie Pie and Princess Skystar the Seapony! Write about one of your holiday friendships.

....

....

....

....

....

....

Wanderlust

Where in the world would your dream adventure take you?

....

How long would you be gone?

....

What would you stay in?

....

Who would go with you?

....

What would you do?

....

You can only take ONE of these items with you. Tick which one you would choose:

⬤ Book ⬤ Hairdryer ⬤ Photo album ⬤ Your pet ⬤ Your favourite food

ALL MAPPED OUT

Twilight Sparkle loves looking at the books of maps in the library. Draw a map of your local area for Twilight, marking all the main sights and buildings so she'll be able to find her way around.

Adventures

Mark your house with a heart!

What are the top 3 sights of your area that Twilight shouldn't miss?

Sight: ....

Why she should visit: ....

Sight: ....

Why she should visit: ....

Sight: ....

Why she should visit: ....

Recording your adventures on a world map is a great way of making sure you never forget them! Stick a map on your bedroom wall, and mark any countries you've been to with a pencil or drawing pin.

What three countries are you desperate to visit?

....

....

....

Mark these in another colour on your map!

I could totally race an aeroplane!

Close your eyes and let your finger fall on the map.
Write down the country you landed on to see where fate would take you....

....

Write down the names of three countries you've never heard of, and then look them up or ask about them.

Country: ....
What did you learn? ....
Would you like to go there on holiday?   ◯ Yes   ◯ No

Country: ....
What did you learn? ....
Would you like to go there on holiday?   ◯ Yes   ◯ No

Country: ....
What did you learn? ....
Would you like to go there on holiday?   ◯ Yes   ◯ No

Travel tales

The Mane 6 travel by airship, balloon, and even on a windmill to save the princesses! Tick all of the types of transport that you've been on:

- ○ Car
- ○ Bus
- ○ Plane
- ○ Boat
- ○ Train
- ○ Hot-air balloon
- ○ Bicycle
- ○ Helicopter

Write down any unusual vehicles you've been on, like a tandem bicycle or a cable car.

....
....
....

What's the longest journey you've ever been on, and where were you going?

....
....
....

Would you like to go on a daredevil flight with Rainbow Dash?

- ○ When can we go?!
- ○ No way!

What is your journey to school like? Who do you travel with?

....
....
....
....

What do you like to do when travelling?

- ○ Play games
- ○ Watch films
- ○ Listen to music
- ○ Look out of the window
- ○ Eat snacks
- ○ Read
- ○ Take a nap
- ○ Chat

Would you love to be taken to school in a stretch limo instead?

- ○ Yes please!
- ○ No thanks!

Twilight Sparkle needs you to go with her on a dangerous mission! When will you be ready?

○ There's no time to lose, let's go now!

○ First I need to pack — I can take four suitcases, right?

○ Dangerous you say? Think I'd better stay at home ...

Write down the songs that would be on your ultimate travel playlist:

....

....

....

....

....

....

You're travelling to visit Princess Celestia. How would you like to get there?

○ On horseback   ○ In a carriage   ○ On foot

What was your worst journey EVER?

....

What happened?

There's only one way to travel — **in style!**

....

....

....

Story scribbler

Even if you don't go far, adventures make AWESOME stories! Write your own exciting tale with you as the star, using your next journey as inspiration.

What's the next journey you will take?

Going to: ....

Travelling by: ....

The start

Answer these questions to set the scene.
What's the weather like?

....

What can you see and hear?

....

....

Who is with you? They will be your main characters.

....

Will your story have magic in it?
O Yes   O No

Will there be a villain to defeat?
O Yes   O No

The middle

This is where the main excitement will happen!
Think of something that suddenly goes wrong or stops your journey.

....

How do you and your main characters react?

....

....

Do you have a plan?

....

The end
Your story will finish as the journey comes to an end.
Describe how the problem was resolved:

Will everyone live happily ever after?
◯ Yes ◯ No

....

....

Is the journey finished?

....

What happens when you arrive at your destination?

....

Now write your full story here! If you run out of room, continue on a piece of paper.

Swell story, sugarcube!

Boredom-busting games

If you ever get super-bored on long journeys, Spike's here to save the day! He's put together these games that are perfect for playing with your pals.

Who am I?

You could ask "Do I have wings?" or "Can I use magic?"

Write the name of one of the Mane 6 on a sticky note and ask your friends to do the same. Then all swap notes (without looking!) and stick the one you get to your forehead. Take turns asking "yes or no" questions to the others to try to guess your pony. Whoever gets theirs right in the least number of questions is the winner!

PONY PAIRS

Cover all the ponies with small pieces of paper, and playing with a friend take turns removing one piece from each page. If the ponies match, keep the paper and give yourself a point. If they don't, replace the paper and keep playing until all the pairs have been found!

Hearts and crosses

Playing with a friend, take turns drawing your symbol in the grid. The first to get three in a row horizontally, vertically or diagonally wins!

Does anypony want to play I SPY?

⚓ Travel companions

Twilight's adventures just wouldn't be the same without her best pals by her side. Which of your friends would you choose to take with you on each of these journeys?

You're going on an action-packed adventure holiday where you'll go rock climbing and canoeing. You'll want to bring an active friend with you!

I'd take: ....

Because: ....

....

You need a friend to take to a music festival. It will be loud and dirty, but who would make it fun?

I'd take: ....

Because: ....

....

You've got two tickets for an around-the-world trip that lasts two whole months! An easy-going friend would be perfect.

I'd take: ....

Because: ....

....

You're off to the beach for a week of reading and lounging by the sea. Who would you take?

I'd take: ....

Because: ....

....

Time for a city break, where the plan is to shop till you drop! Who would be the perfect companion?

I'd take: ....

Because: ....

....

Now describe a dream group holiday for you and your friends.

Where would you sleep?

What would you eat?

What would you do?

EQUESTRIA
and beyond!

The ponies visit some new places on their way to find the Queen of the Hippogriffs, but sometimes there's no place like home! Read their travel guide to their most memorable destinations, then decide if you'd like to visit, too.

CANTERLOT

The capital city of Equestria, Canterlot is home to Princess Celestia and Princess Luna. It's fast-paced and bustling, and holds all the most important pony events, such as the Friendship Festival.

Your rating: Boo! ★★★★★ Yay!

Would you like to visit?: ⬤ Yes   ⬤ No

Why?: ....

KLUGETOWN

Klugetown is a trading village outside Equestria with a bit of a fearsome reputation. It's a little scary, but you certainly wouldn't get bored — and you could visit Capper!

Your rating: Boo! ★★★★★ Yay!

Would you like to visit?: ⬤ Yes   ⬤ No

Why?: ....

Seapony Village Ponyville Adventures

SEAPONY VILLAGE

The Seaponies live in a totally awesome underwater paradise! It has a secret entrance through a fountain, and Queen Novo may even turn you into a Seapony for your visit.

Your rating: **Boo!** ★★★★★ **Yay!**

Would you like to visit?:　　Yes ◯　　　　No ◯

Why?: ....

PONYVILLE

Ponyville is a small town that's home to Twilight Sparkle and her friends. Highlights include Applejack's barn (ask her to give you the tasting menu), and Pinkie Pie's house, where there's always a party!

Your rating: **Boo!** ★★★★★ **Yay!**

Would you like to visit?:　　Yes ◯　　　　No ◯

Why?: ....

A week of adventures

You don't need to travel to have an adventure! Just follow these ideas from the Mane 6 for an action-packed week with your pals....

Monday
Rainbow Dash likes to start the week by being active! Go roller-skating, cycling, or just play catch in the park with your friends.

Tuesday
What better way to spend a Tuesday than having a Swap Party? Rarity asks everypony to bring make-up tips, new hairstyle ideas or clothes to swap with the group. Give it a try!

Wednesday
Follow Fluttershy's lead and spend time with animals. You could feed the ducks in the park, or visit an animal sanctuary. Cute!

Thursday
Twilight Sparkle suggests starting your very own book club. Ask each of your friends to read the same book, and then have a meeting to talk about what you all liked and didn't like about it.

Friday
It's party time! Throw a sleepover for your friends with all your favourite games and snacks. Pinkie Pie approves!

Saturday
According to Applejack, Saturdays are just made for picnics! Pack a bagful of tasty treats, and spread a blanket in a sunny spot.

Sunday
Finish the week by making an AWESOME ADVENTURE TREASURE HUNT....

AWESOME **ADVENTURE** TREASURE HUNT

Step 1

Choose your prizes! Ideas could include chocolate bars, friendship bracelets or flower posies:

....

....

....

Step 2

Tuck the prizes out of sight in different places. It's a good idea to choose one area, like a house or garden. Record where you've hidden them here:

....

....

....

Step 3

Write clues for where each prize is hidden on card and cut them out. Give the first clue to your friends, then hide the second with your first prize. That clue will lead to your second prize, and so on. Write your clues here:

....

....

....

You could have rhyming clues. For example, "Where you rest your head, it's under the ...." or draw a special treasure map for your friends instead! ♥

Best week EVER!

Your perfect holiday

Take this quiz to find out what sort of holiday suits you best!

Adventures

1 You've just arrived in Canterlot.
What's the first thing you do?
a. Zoom up to the clouds. Aerial acrobatics, anyone?
b. Find the nearest yoga class — I need to unwind after the journey!
c. Go straight to Canterlot Castle, it'll make an AWESOME photo.
d. Put my hooves up and see if I can get a taste of Applejack's famous pie....

The best holidays are:
○ With family
○ With friends

2 It's your first night in the city. Where will you sleep?
a. Sleep? There are too many activities to cram in!
b. Princess Celestia will let me stay in the castle, right?
c. Somewhere near the centre, so I can plan a full day of sightseeing.
d. Any comfy bed would be great, and a bonus if I can see the stars!

3 Rise and shine! What's for breakfast?
a. Whatever I can grab on the way to my hot-air balloon ride!
b. Show me to the nearest 5* restaurant.
c. Anything that the locals eat.
d. Something simple, but LOTS of it.

Would you rather
go on holiday:
○ Somewhere hot
○ Somewhere cold

4 You have the whole day ahead of you. What activities do you have planned?
a. ALL the activities!
b. Shopping, or a visit to the salon.
c. I need to soak up all the culture of Canterlot! Is there a tour?
d. Does napping count as an activity?

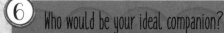

5 You can take one day trip from Canterlot. Where will you go?
a. Klugetown for sure. It won't be dull!
b. To Crystal Empire. That place is FABULOUS.
c. I'd love to see the Seapony Kingdom. Imagine the history!
d. I've got everything I need right here!

6 Who would be your ideal companion?
a. Rainbow Dash could show me her moves.
b. Rarity — that pony has style.
c. Twilight Sparkle knows all the sights.
d. Fluttershy. She's nice and quiet!

Answers:

Mostly a's
Adventure holiday
You're a true thrill-seeker and love being active on trips! Anywhere you can go bungee jumping, white-water rafting or skydiving would be PERFECT for you.

Mostly b's
Spa retreat
You love to be pampered, and a holiday is a great excuse to relax in luxury. A fancy hotel or resort (close to shops, naturally) would suit you just fine!

Mostly c's
City break
Sightseeing and exploring new places appeals to you, and you get excited about discovering new cultures. A city break would be the ideal match for your curious and adventurous nature.

Mostly d's
Beach holiday
To you, a holiday means lots of rest and relaxation! You would love lying on a beach listening to the sound of the waves, with lots of tasty food and a comfy bed at night. Bliss!

PIRATE PASSPORT!

Only the toughest ponies can last in pirate-filled skies. Captain Celaeno has invited you to take a trip aboard her airship, but first you need a pirate identity!

Start with your pirate name! Come up with your own, or put together three from this list:

Title	First name	Second name
Captain	Glitter	Tail
First mate	Butter	Fingers
Master	Strong	Wings
Cabinpony	Sea	Storm
Pirate	Pony	Pants

Now fill in your travel document.

Draw a picture of yourself as a pirate here!

Pirate name: ....

Pirate job: ....

Pirate age: ....

Ship name: ....

Parrot colours: ....

Favourite treasure: ....

Design your own AWESOME airship so you can be just like the pirates.

Will you have a flag?

Don't forget to colour it in!

Pirate chic is all the rage!

Where would you fly first in your airship?

....

Who would be your crew?

....

....

....

Wanderlust

Use this space to create your own travel pin board by sticking in pictures of places you want to go someday....

It don't need to be someplace fancy to be special.

Fly forward a couple of pages to play a magical board game!

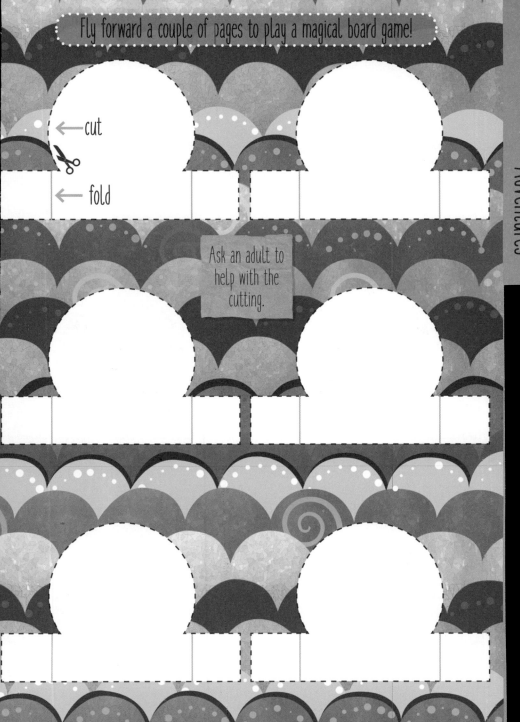

← cut

← fold

Ask an adult to help with the cutting.

Adventures

COUNTERS

Adventures

Fluttershy

Applejack

Rarity

Twilight Sparkle

Rainbow Dash

Pinkie Pie

Race to Canterlot
board game

Will you make it to the castle in time to defeat the Storm King and free the princesses?

> Princess Celestia needs our help!

What you'll need:

• 1 dice
• Friends to play the game with — up to six can join in, but two will work just fine!

Before you begin:

Decide who will be which character or pick out of a hat.
Cut out the game pieces and fold along the lines.
Take turns rolling the dice. Whoever gets the highest number will go first, then it will be the turn of the pony player on the left.

How to play:

Place all game pieces on the 'Start' square.
Each pony player then takes a turn rolling the dice, and moves the number of squares shown.
Watch out for special instruction squares. These could be traps laid by the Storm King's cronies, or even magic to help you on your journey. If you land on one, read and follow the instructions.

ADVENTURE IS CALLING ... ARE YOU READY TO GO?

START
1
2
You spot a town and speed up. Move forward two spaces.
3
You're wandering the desert for AGES and need to rest. Miss a turn.
Capper at your service!
Woo-hoo, let's go!
4
5
6
THE MAGIC OF FRIENDSHIP
Anypony who lands here can choose whether to activate the spell to bring all players to this square.
I'm gonna need you ponies to surrender.
7
8
You've entered Klugetown, but nopony will help you! Move back a space.
9
10
Tempest is hot on your tracks – you should lie low. Miss a turn.
11
12
Capper points you in the right direction. Take another turn.
13

Beautiful bedroom

Capper's lair contains all kinds of baubles and trinkets from his travels. Turn your bedroom into a real adventurer's space just like his with these decoration ideas.

Use a piece of string or ribbon and some pegs to create a great photo display for all your favourite pics. Stretch it along a wall, using sticky tape or drawing pins to secure.

Make an awesome hanging decoration using old maps. Choose a shape like hearts or flowers and cut lots of them out from the map. Create a hole in the middle of the shapes and thread onto string until it's the length you like. Voila!

Create a collage of amazing places by cutting out pictures from magazines and arranging them on a piece of cardboard. Hang on your door for an instant adventurer feel.

Use old shoeboxes as Memory Boxes to hold souvenirs from all of your trips. Decorate them to look like old suitcases by covering with coloured paper and using a thick felt pen to add cool details like buckles and straps. Stack them up for an awesome effect!

Design your DREAM bedroom here. You could paint stars on the ceiling or have a magical princess canopy ... the only limit is your imagination!

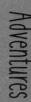

Simply gorgeous!

THINKING FAST

The Mane 6 were busy planning the Friendship Festival, when all of a sudden Tempest arrived to capture the princesses! How would you use your brainpower if adventure came calling unexpectedly?

Tempest has appeared in your bedroom — you need to get out of there!
There's no time to pack, but you can grab FOUR items from your surroundings.
What do you choose and why?

I'd bring..

Because..

....

I'd bring..

Because..

....

I'd bring..

Because..

....

I'd bring..

Because..

....

You're travelling across the desert in search of help.
Can you use any of your items to help you get food or drink?

I'd use ....

By ....

....

Picture of my sister Maud, anyone?

You've arrived in Klugetown and need directions, but the scary traders
will only help you if you have something good to trade!

I'd trade ....

Because ....

....

You've managed to get a lift with the pirates to Mount Aris, but they're feeling glum. Could you use any of your three remaining items to cheer them up?

I'd use ....

By ....

....

....

You're at the secret fountain entrance to the Seapony Kingdom, but there's nopony around! How could you use your items to get attention?

I'd use ....

By ....

....

....

Twilight Sparkle has been kidnapped! Will any of your items help you get her back from Tempest?

I'd use ....

By ....

....

....

You've rescued Twilight, and everything is back to normal in time for the Friendship Festival. Can you use your items to have fun?

I'd use ....

By ....

....

....

Adventure journal

Use these pages to plan and record a whole year of your adventures, from small trips and journeys to weekend breaks and holidays!

January

February

March

April

May

June

Write the plans you'd love to make in pencil, and the ones that are definitely happening in pen.
At the end of each month, write a line or two about the adventures you had.

July

August

September

October

November

December

What adventure are you most looking forward to?

....

Special souvenirs

Keeping mementos can help you remember the adventures you have with your friends! Tickets, photos, feathers and leaves all make great souvenirs. Stick some of your keepsakes below.

It can be fun to choose an item like magnets or postcards, and collect one from every place you go!

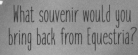

What souvenir would you bring back from Equestria?

....

Shoe wings!

Make sure you always travel in style by adding a pair of shoe wings to your favourite trainers. You can use them as a template, so why not make a pair for each of your friends?

• Cut along the dotted lines to get the template for your shoe wings, then stick to a piece of thin card.

• Cut round each wing again, then ask an adult to cut out the lace holes for you.

• If you'd like to make other pairs, trace round your wings on to more pieces of card.

Ask an adult to help with the cutting.

• Thread your laces through the holes, and you're ready to fly off on your next adventure!

Colour your shoe wings or decorate them with glitter!

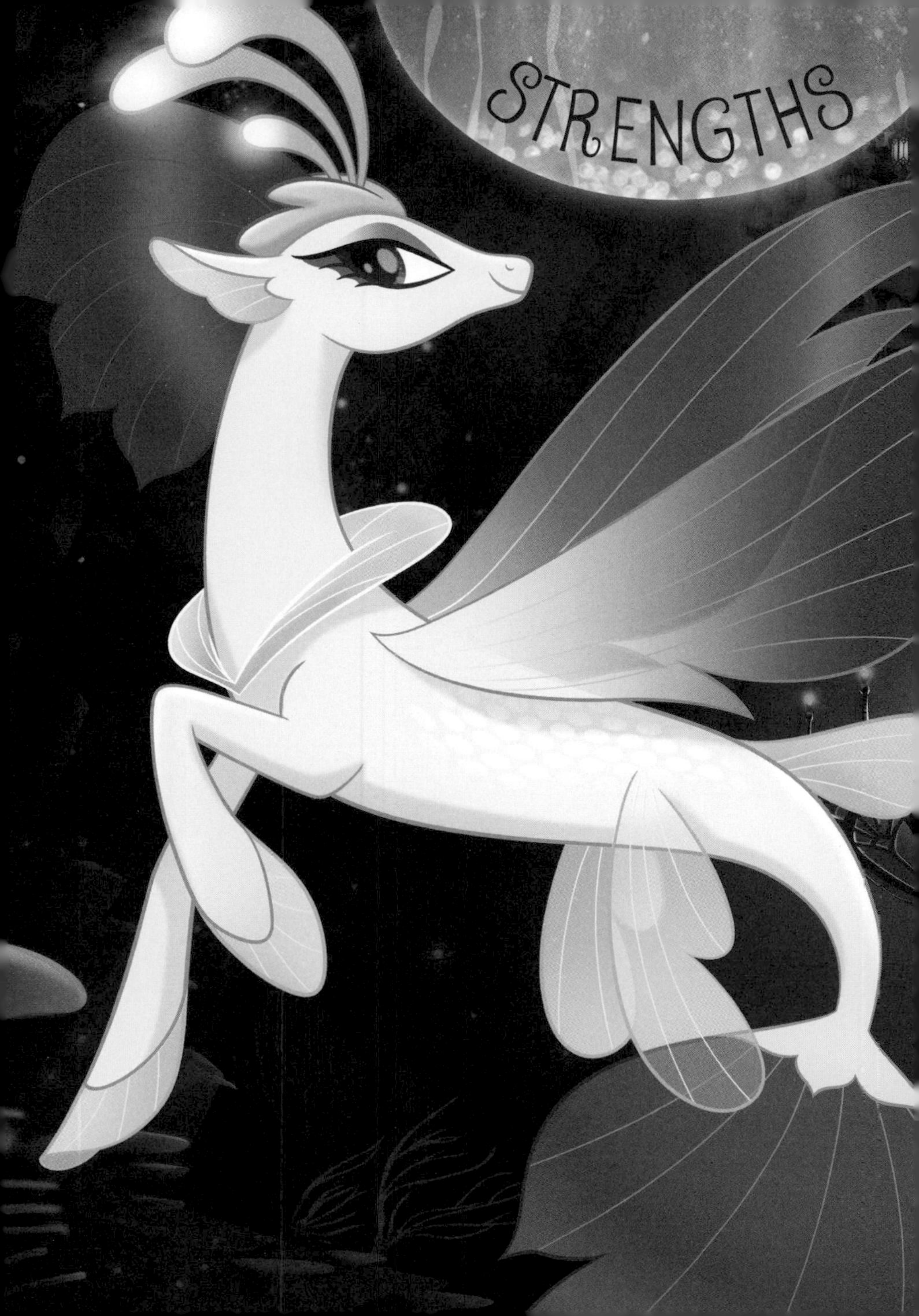
STRENGTHS

Family matters

Families are a super-duper source of strength because they offer advice, support and tons of encouragement. The ponies want to know all about YOUR special family.

Draw or stick a picture here!

Draw or stick a picture here!

Name: ....

Age: ....

Relation: ....

Name: ....

Age: ....

Relation: ....

Draw or stick a picture here!

Draw or stick a picture here!

Name: ....

Age: ....

Relation: ....

Name: ....

Age: ....

Relation: ....

Draw or stick a picture here!

Draw or stick a picture here!

Name: ....
Age: ....
Relation: ....

Name: ....
Age: ....
Relation: ....

Draw or stick a picture here!

Draw or stick a picture here!

Name: ....
Age: ....
Relation: ....

Name: ....
Age: ....
Relation: ....

WHAT'S YOUR *friendship* STRENGTH?

The Mane 6 are best pals, but their unique personalities mean they're each a different kind of friend. Take this quiz to discover YOUR friendship strength.

One of your friends is upset. How do you help?
a. Gather your group of friends so you can talk about it with her — you're all in it together!
b. Listen to her problem, with tissues on hand.
c. Suggest playing a super-fun game to cheer her up.
d. Leave her alone — she knows you're there if she needs you.

It's your friend's birthday, woo-hoo! Have you:
a. Organized a group outing or special sleepover with her closest pals.
b. Given her a handmade card or thoughtful gift you know will mean a lot to her.
c. Thrown her a CRAZY party complete with cake cannon, inviting everyone you know.
d. Totally forgotten it was her birthday ... but you'll make it up to her!

Somepony is being mean to your friend. What do you do?
a. Try to reason with the bully. They'll listen, especially if you have your buddies for back-up.
b. Ignore the meanie and make sure your friend is OK.
c. Make a joke to lighten the mood!
d. Someone better hold you back — how DARE they attack your pal!

Your friend has spilled one of your secrets when she pony-promised not to tell. Do you:
a. Calmly let her know you're upset, and ask her to apologize.
b. Hear her out — she's bound to have a good reason.
c. Brush it off. She's a great friend and you forgive her.
d. This is NOT COOL. She's got some grovelling to do!

A friend has been KIDNAPPED! What do you do?
a. Grab the rest of the gang, pronto — you need a rescue plan!
b. Panic! You're worried about your friend, but you're scared, too.
c. ROAD TRIP! Who says a rescue mission can't also be fun?
d. You're already on her trail, and will have her back in no time.

Life would be boring if everypony were the same!

Mostly a's

The leader
You're the glue that holds the group together, and your friends look up to you. You appreciate each individual, and are often the one making sure everypony is included. You're confident, patient and organized.

Mostly b's

The supporter
Everypony comes to you for the great advice you give, and knows you'll have a shoulder to cry on. You're good at keeping secrets and always trust your friends. You're kind, caring and a great listener.

Mostly c's

The joker
You can make everypony laugh, even when they're feeling sad! You always look on the bright side, and often think up great new activities for your group to do together. You're cheerful, positive and full of fun.

Mostly d's

The warrior
People may think you're tough, but you have a real soft spot for your friends. You're the first to stand up for your pals, and are very protective! You're adventurous, brave and fiercely loyal.

STRENGTHS

YOUR STRENGTHS

There are so many special things about you that make you awesome! Tell the ponies all about them here....

People often compliment you on: ....
....
....

You give really good advice about: ....
....
....

A time when somepony said they were proud of you: ....
....
....

A time when you were proud of yourself: ....
....
....

People always go to you for help with: ....
....
....

Do you have a hidden talent?: ....
....
....

Are you a good listener?
○ Yes   ○ No

Are you good at making friends?
○ Yes   ○ No

Do you tell HILARIOUS jokes?
○ Yes   ○ No

Do you have an eye for fashion, darling?
○ Yes   ○ No

Are you great at reading?
○ Yes   ○ No

Are you good with animals?
○ Yes   ○ No

Are you fast like me?
○ Yes   ○ No

Can y'all bake?
○ Yes   ○ No

Are you loyal to your friends?
○ Yes   ○ No

Can you keep secrets?
○ Yes   ○ No

Are you a whizz with computers?
○ Yes   ○ No

Can you sing?
○ Yes   ○ No

STRENGTHS

The Elements of Harmony

The Elements of Harmony represent the most powerful magic known to ponydom — but only if they are united. Award an element to yourself and your friends by deciding who best matches each. Together, you can do anything!

HONESTY
The element of honesty is awarded to ....
for ....

KINDNESS
The element of kindness is awarded to ....
for ....

LOYALTY
The element of loyalty is awarded to ....
for ....

GENEROSITY
The element of generosity is awarded to ....
for ....

LAUGHTER
The element of laughter is awarded to ....
for ....

MAGIC
The element of magic is awarded to ....
for ....

Friendship
charms

Fill out a diamond for each friend, then cut out along the dotted lines. Tie a ribbon through the holes to make a cute friendship keepsake to present your pals!

To: ....
You are *awesome* because:
....
....
....

To: ....
You are *awesome* because:
....
....
....

To: ....
You are *awesome* because:
....
....
....

Ask an adult to help with the cutting.

To: ....
You are *awesome* because:
....
....

To: ....
You are *awesome* because:
....
....

STRENGTHS

Share the love

Your friends think you're pretty amazing, too. Honest! Ask each of your friends to pick a strip on the opposite page and write a word that describes you in the space.

STRENGTHS

Ask an adult to help with the cutting.

Glue here

Glue here

Glue here

Glue here

Glue here

Paper heart garland

When the strips have been filled in on both sides, turn them into a pony-tastic paper heart garland!

INSTRUCTIONS

Step 1. Ask an adult to help you cut along the dotted lines of each strip.

Step 2. Fold your first strip in half. Hold the crease of the strip between your thumb and forefinger.

Step 3. Bend the two ends of your strip to make a heart shape, then secure by putting glue on your glue tab.

How charming this would look hung up in your bedroom!

Step 4. Fold your second strip in half, then link through your first heart.

GLUE

Step 5. Bend the two ends of your second strip and stick together to make another heart.

Step 6. Repeat steps 4 and 5 until you've used all your strips and have a chain of hearts, one from each of your best pals.

Make the chain super-long by adding more of your own hearts!

Create your Cutie Mark

It's time you earned your very own Cutie Mark! Answer the questions to give you inspiration, then draw your own special design.

Many Cutie Marks have just two colours — which are your favourites?

.... and ....

Which of your strengths do you think best describes you?

....

What do you want other ponies to know about you before you speak to them?

....

....

Would you like an object or animal as your Cutie Mark?

⚪ Object ⚪ Animal

Would your prefer your Mark to be simple or detailed?

⚪ Detailed ⚪ Simple

Do you want your Mark to be pretty or cool?

○ COOL ○ Pretty

What's your absolute FAVOURITE thing?

....

....

....

Draw your Cutie Mark here!

Don't forget to colour in your Cutie Mark!

STRENGTHS

Pony predictions

Princess Luna often stargazes at night, imagining the future of ponies all over Equestria. Where do you think you and your pals will be ten years from now?

ME

I will live in: ....

With: ....

My job will be: ....

Because: ....

....

....

Draw a picture of the future you here!

MY MANE 5

Name: ....

She will live in: ....

Her job will be: ....

Because: ....

....

Name: ....

She will live in: ....

Her job will be: ....

Because: ....

....

Name: ....

She will live in: ....

Her job will be: ....

Because: ....

....

It would be really cool to take these predictions to your friendship reunion, to see how many came true!

I see great things for you ponies!

Name: ....

She will live in: ....

Her job will be: ....

Because: ....

....

Name: ....

She will live in: ....

Her job will be: ....

Because: ....

....

Most likely to ...

Most likely to win an Oscar: ....

Most likely to own their own business: ....

Most likely to travel the world: ....

Most likely to get married: ....

Most likely to become prime minister: ....

Riding high QUIZ

A strong pony like you is bound to make waves wherever you go! Take this quiz to discover what kind of success your strengths will bring you.

STRENGTHS

Would you say you're ambitious?

YES

NO

Do you prefer working alone to working in a team?

YES

NO

Would telling somepony what to do make you feel nervous?

NO

YES

Do you HATE arguments?

NO

YES

Is being kind way more important than being noticed?

YES

NO

Would being away from home for a long time make you sad?

YES

NO

Do you dream of huge crowds cheering your name?

YES

NO

Are you good at giving advice?

NO

YES

Would you choose to go to a party rather than finishing your homework?

YES

NO

Is being liked important to you?

NO

YES

You will be ...

Do you love being the centre of attention?

YES

NO

Are you great at performing?

YES

NO

Are you super-competitive?

YES

NO

NO

Would you give up something you REALLY wanted, if a friend wanted it too?

YES

NO

POWERFUL

You're happy to take the lead, and don't mind if that sometimes makes you unpopular. You'll grow into a force to be reckoned with, just like Tempest — but remember that power can be used for good as well as evil.

Famous

You were born to perform, and feel totally at home on the stage. Whether it's singing, dancing or acting, you've got the talent and determination to succeed. Songbird Serenade better watch out!

Admired

Like Twilight Sparkle, friends and family are close to your heart. All you want in life is to make them proud, and with your endless loyalty and kindness you won't fail!

ROLE MODEL

Twilight Sparkle looks up to Princess Celestia, and hopes that she'll grow to be just like her. Having a role model can help you become somepony you're proud of. Choose someone special as your role model, and write all about them below.

The name of my role model is:

....

I admire them because:

....

....

Three strengths they have that I respect are:

....

....

How I can be more like them:

....

....

....

Draw or stick a picture of your special person here!

Your role model can be real or from a story, a family member, celebrity or even your favourite pony!

Dream BIG

You're the star of your very own adventure, and it can take you down any path you choose. Light up Canterlot by writing a wish for the future on each of the stars in the sky....

Wishes made on shooting stars hold a special kind of magic.

A year of awesome

Dreaming big is amazing, but teeny-tiny dreams are at the heart of every great achievement. Turn your year into twelve mini adventures by setting yourself a pony-tastic goal for each month. You can do anything you set your mind to!

January

February

March

April

You could help around your home without being asked.

Do something scary, like entering a competition or joining a school club!

Read a whole SHELFFUL of books.

May

June

July

August

September

October

November

December

Donate some of your old clothes to charity, darling.

Make friends with somepony (or even better, somePONIES) you don't know.

Wake up early to see a swell sunrise.

Daydreaming

Rainbow Dash always dreamed of becomi
a member of the Wonderbolts, the total
awesome aerial acrobatic squad, and
she did! Join her in Cloudsdale
by adding your daydreams....

Draw or describe you in your
DREAM JOB.

Draw or describe your
DREAM PET.

I happen to know
that dragons make
excellent pets!

DREAMS

Would you rather be ...
○ Happy ○ Successful

Cars can have wings, right?

Draw or describe your DREAM CAR.

Which would be cooler to live in?
○ A castle   ○ A treehouse

Draw or describe your DREAM HOUSE.

DREAMS

DISCOVER YOUR FORTUNE

Have a question about the future that you REALLY want to know the answer to?
Wonder no more! Create this magical fortune-teller to reveal all.

How to make:

1. Ask an adult to help cut out the fortune-teller, then place it decorated side face up.
2. Fold each corner into the centre to make a diamond shape.
3. Flip it over, and fold the new corners into the middle again.
4. Fold the square in half.
5. Put your thumbs and forefingers under each flap, and push the four corners together then apart to make your fortune-teller open and close.

Share with your pals, and record your results here:

Name: ....
Fortune: ....

....

Name: ....
Fortune: ....

....

Name: ....
Fortune: ....

....

Name: ....
Fortune: ....

....

Name: ....
Fortune: ....

....

Name: ....
Fortune: ....

....

DREAMS

How to play:

♥ Ask the fortune-teller a "yes or no" question about your future.

♥ Choose a pony princess and spell her name out loud, opening and closing the fortune-teller for each letter. L-U-N-A would mean you open and close your fortune-teller four times.

♥ Then pick a number and open and close the fortune-teller that number of times.

♥ Now choose another number, and lift the flap to reveal the answer to your question.

Ask an adult to help with the cutting ✂

BUCKET LIST

The Mane 6 never planned to leave Equestria, but the incredible people and places they visited made their ponyquest totally worth it! Make a list of the things you want to see and do throughout your own epic life adventure.

Watch out, world!

DREAMS

Dream diary

The dreams you have when you're asleep can have surprising and powerful meanings. Whether you dream about epic ponyquests like Rainbow Dash or simply eating pie like Applejack, record a whole week of your dreams here.

Monday

Keep this book by your bed, so you can scribble down your dreams as soon as you wake up.

Tuesday

Aim for 8 hours of sleep a night. Well-reste ponies are more likely to remember their dreams.

Wednesday

Thursday

Friday

Saturday

Sunday

Tell yourself you're going to remember your dreams just before you go to sleep each night.

Even if you can't remember the whole dream, write down any feelings or people you think of when you wake up.

I once dreamed I was runnin' from a crabby old unicorn who wanted to take over Equestria! Wait....

DREAMS

Sleeping secrets

Twilight Sparkle has found a book of dream meanings in the library! Read on to discover what your dreams say about you....

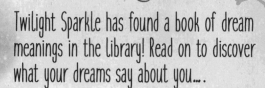

Draw a circle around the dreams that you've had!

Water

Water in dreams can represent your emotions, so the type of water is important! A waterfall might mean you should go with the flow, and a stormy ocean could show that you're feeling a bit unsettled.

Flying

If you were dreaming of soaring high in the sky like a Pegasus, chances are you're super-happy right now! Maybe you achieved a goal or aced a test in school, but whatever it is, you're on cloud nine.

Animals

An animal dream can help you discover the things you secretly want and need — even before you know them yourself. Is the animal big and strong? You might be looking for protection. Is it small and gentle? You need to be treated with kindness.

A bridge

Dreaming of a bridge could show that you're about to enter a new chapter of your life. Maybe something big at school or home is going to change, or perhaps you're about to go on a ponyquest!

Being chased

If you're being chased in your dream, it might mean that you're running away from something in real life. Is there anything you're worried about? Talking to friends or a teacher will help you feel less anxious.

EMBARRASSING DREAMS

Have you ever dreamed ...

Oh, the horror!

That you needed the toilet, but couldn't find one?

○ Yes   ○ No

That you were in a public place WITH NO CLOTHES ON?

○ Yes   ○ No

BEST AND WORST

Draw or write about the BEST dream you've ever had:

Now draw or describe your SCARIEST nightmare:

If you have a lot of bad dreams, try to avoid eating before bed.

WIDE AWAKE

Everypony has nights where they just CAN'T get to sleep. Next time you're tossing and turning, help your worries float away by counting the pirates and Pegasus ponies.

DREAMS

The ponies are bouncing from the page to your room ... you are feeling very sleepy ... BOING! Boing! Boing! Boing!

Mysterious message

Capper is a very crafty cat, and often sends messages he doesn't want anyone else to read. His top tip is to create a secret code by drawing your own symbol for each letter of the alphabet. Sneaky!

My code

A=   F=   K=   P=   U=

B=   G=   L=   Q=   V=

C=   H=   M=   R=   W=

D=   I=   N=   S=   X=

E=   J=   O=   T=   Y=

                                                Z=

Share this key with FRIENDS ONLY, then use the opposite page to write them a top-secret message. Make it extra secure by following Capper's instructions to fold your note into an envelope.

1. Ask an adult to help you cut out your letter.

2. Place your letter white side up, and follow the dashed lines to fold both top corners into the center to make a triangle at the top.

3. Fold the two long edges of the paper inwards.

4. Fold the bottom section of of the letter upwards, so that it meets the bottom of your triangle.

5. Now fold the triangle down to make the flap of the envelope!

Seal with a sticker, so you'll know if it's been opened!

Knock, knock

Perfect for sleepovers!

This awesome door hanger will make sure nopony disturbs you when you're swapping secrets with your pals. Cut along the dotted line, hang on your bedroom door and then gossip away!

Ask an adult to help with the cutting.

Shh ... secret sharing in progress.
COME BACK LATER!

Welcome, everypony!

Invisible ink

You don't need magic to make your writing invisible – just follow these simple steps to make some super-secret ink. The Storm King himself couldn't read your words unless you told him how!

WHAT YOU'LL NEED:

- Half a lemon   · Water   · Spoon   · Bowl
- · Cotton bud   · White paper   · Torch

1. Squeeze some lemon juice into the bowl and add a few drops of water.
2. Mix the water and lemon juice with the spoon.
3. Dip the cotton bud into the mixture and write a message on a piece of paper.
4. Wait for the juice to dry so it becomes completely invisible.
5. When you are ready to read your secret message or show it to someone else, warm the paper by holding it close to a torch.

Test your ink by writing a secret message to Rainbow Dash here:

Make it DOUBLY secret by writing in code as well. Take that, Storm King!

Apples of admiration

As the spirit of honesty, Applejack knows how to tell it like it is! Follow her lead by writing down the things you secretly admire about your family and friends — but have never told them.

Name:

....

What I admire about them:

....

....

....

....

....

....

Name:

....

What I admire about them:

....

....

....

....

....

Name:

....

What I admire about them:

....

....

....

....

Name:

What I admire about them:

....
....
....
....
....

Name: ....

What I admire about them:

....
....
....
....

Name:

What I admire about them:

....
....
....
....

How 'bout you share these here apples with the nice folk you mention?

My secrets

The Mane 6 know how to keep each others' secrets, and would rather be handed over to Grubber and his cronies than break a pony promise! Share YOUR secrets here.

Something you're scared of:

Something only your best friend knows:

Something you didn't get caught for:

Something that's secretly making you happy:

OK, OK, it was me who ate the jewels from Rarity's curtains!

Something you've never told anypony:

HOW EMBARRASSING!

The last time you tripped over:

Something uncool that you secretly like:

Your music guilty pleasure:

Something that makes you blush:

The most embarrassing thing that's EVER happened to you:

EVERYTHING makes me blush!

Your pony identity

You and your Mane 5 each have a secret pony identity that's just waiting to be discovered! Follow the steps below to reveal how you'd be known in Equestria....

Your pony type

Your birthday decides what type of pony you are. Which month were you born in?

January, February, March: **Seapony**

April, May, June: **Earth pony**

July, August, September: **Unicorn**

October, November, December: **Pegasus**

Your pony name

Your name holds the key to what your pony-persona is called. Awesome, right?

Your first name begins with:

A : Acorn
B : Butterfly
C : Cinnamon
D : Dazzling
E : Emerald
F : Flutter
G : Glimmer
H : Honey
I : Ice cream
J : Jelly
K : Krystal
L : Lightning
M : Meadow
N : Nettle
O : Orange
P : Phoenix
Q : Quiver
R : Rose
S : Sunshine
T : Twinkle
U : Unicorn
V : Venus
W : Winter
X : Xandria
Y : Yawning
Z : Zodiac

Your last name begins with:

A : Autumn
B : Bloom
C : Cloud
D : Dancer
E : Ember
F : Fizzlepop
G : Glitter
H : Harvest
I : Ivy
J : Jewel
K : Kisses
L : Lily
M : Moon
N : Night
O : Ocean
P : Pie
Q : Queen
R : Ribbon
S : Sparkle
T : Twist
U : Unity
V : Violet
W : Wings
X : X-treme
Y : Yawns
Z : Zen

Secrets

Your pony LOOK

The colour of your hair looks a little different in Equestria. A LOT different, actually!

Your HAIR colour is: | **Your MANE would be:**

Brown ---------------→ Purple
Blonde --------------→ Pink
Red -----------------→ Blue
Black ---------------→ Multicoloured

Your pony hangout

Left-handed ← Are you → Right-handed

You live in Ponyville! You're from Canterlot!

Record your results

Name: ....
My pony type: ....
My pony name: ....
My pony look: ....
My pony hangout: ....

Name: ....
My pony type: ....
My pony name: ....
My pony look: ....
My pony hangout: ....

Name: ....
My pony type: ....
My pony name: ....
My pony look: ....
My pony hangout: ....

Name: ....
My pony type: ....
My pony name: ....
My pony look: ....
My pony hangout: ....

Name: ....
My pony type: ....
My pony name: ....
My pony look: ....
My pony hangout: ....

Name: ....
My pony type: ....
My pony name: ....
My pony look: ....
My pony hangout: ....

SECRET DIARY

The Seaponies are secret-keeping experts, but they've been hidden for such a long time that they're curious about the outside world. Tell them all about a week in your life by keeping a diary.

Monday

....

....

....

....

....

....

....

....

....

....

Make your diary super-mysterious by writing in code or invisible ink.

Tuesday

....

....

....

....

....

....

....

Wednesday

....

....

....

....

....

....

....

....

Thursday

Friday

I tell all my secrets to Shelly and Sheldon ... but they're made of shells and can't talk back.

Saturday

Continue your diary on separate pages or in a notebook.

....
....
....
....
....
....
....

Sunday

....
....
....
....
....
....
....

Secrets

Special surprise

Nothing says "Surprise!" like bursting out of a giant birthday cake with your closest friends as part of an elaborate rescue mission ... but breakfast in bed comes close. Plan a secret morning feast for one of your family members, as a way of telling them they're awesome!

Who I'm going to surprise:...

Because: ....

....

When it'll be: ....

....

Share the secret with an adult, so they can help make the food!

On the menu

To eat:..

....

To drink: ....

....

....

Other details: ....

Putting flowers on their breakfast tray would be super-sweet!

....

How I'll keep it secret:

....

SECRET KEEPER

Queen Novo knows how important a good hiding place is! Keep your secrets as safe as her magic pearl by making this special box to hold them in.

Ask an adult to help with the cutting.

How to make:

1. Cut along the dashed lines to get the outline for your box.
2. Fold along the dotted lines.
3. Put glue on all the PINK tabs — the others are for the hidden lid.
4. Attach tabs to the sides and fill with your secrets!